Truly Madly Deeply

A Couple's Memory Journal

So
why don't we go
SOMEWHERE
ONLY
we know?

Celebrate *the* Past

Chapter 1

When and where we first met:

....
....

You said to me:

....
....

I said to you:

....
....

My first impression was:

....
....
....

Your first impression was:

....
....
....

My heart

was wrapped in clover
the night I looked at you

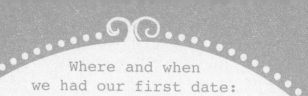

Where and when
we had our first date:

....

....

....

Specific moments I will always remember
about the date:

....

....

....

....

Specific moments you will always remember
about the date:

....

....

....

....

....

All at once, my heart took flight

I first knew I liked you when:

I first knew you liked me when:

We kissed
like we invented it

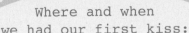

Where and when
we had our first kiss:

....

....

How I would describe our first kiss:

....

....

....

Details I will always remember about this moment:

....

....

....

....

....

....

....

....

My birthday:

My astrological sign:

Your birthday:

Your astrological sign:

The stars were aligned!

From the beginning, there were little signs
that we would end up together, including:

I Can't help
falling in
Love
with you

Details I'll never forget about the first time you told me you loved me:

....
....
....
....
....
....
....
....
....

• FIVE LITTLE THINGS •
YOU DID
THAT MADE ME
FEEL LOVED:

1.

2.

3.

4.

5.

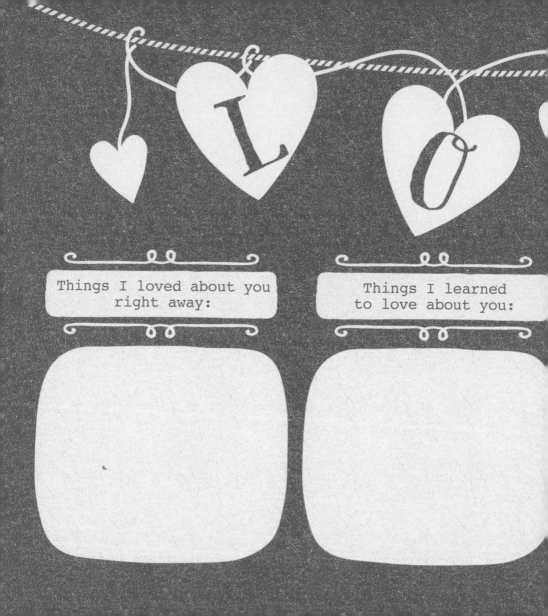

Things I loved about you
right away:

Things I learned
to love about you:

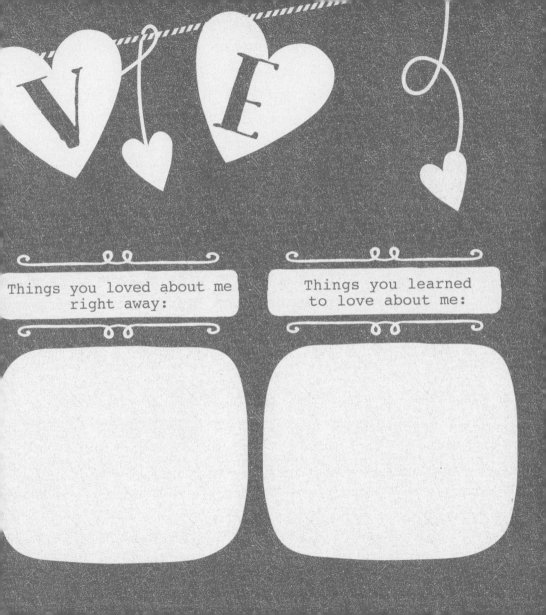

Things you loved about me
right away:

Things you learned
to love about me:

I'm only me
when I'm with you.

The first movie we
watched together was:

....

....

These movies always remind me of you:

....

....

....

....

These actors/characters always remind me of you:

....

....

....

....

....

....

....

THE FIRST CONCERT
we attended together was:

Details I will always remember about that concert:

"Our song"

These songs always remind me of you:

....

....

....

Here's a lyric that expresses how I feel
about you: ....

....

....

....

....

....

MY FAVORITE VACATION WAS

the trip we took to:

My favorite moment was when:

Vacation Spots
I Like

Vacation Spots
We Like

Vacation Spots
You Like

PEOPLE
are strange WHEN
YOU'RE A STRANGER

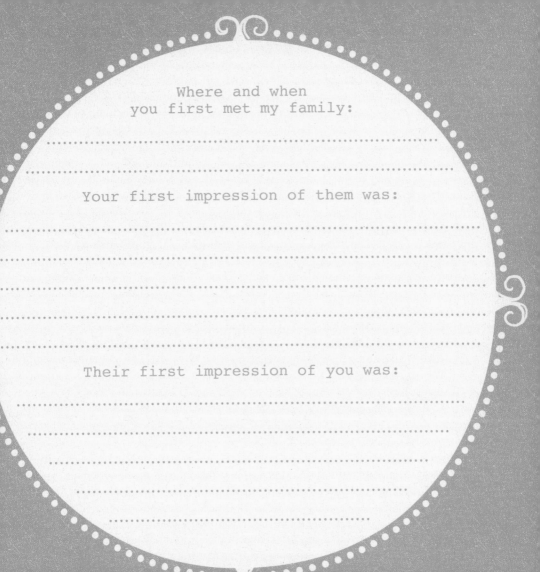

Where and when
you first met my family:

....

....

Your first impression of them was:

....

....

....

....

Their first impression of you was:

....

....

....

....

Where and when I first met your family:

....
....
....
....
....
....
....

I felt welcome when:

....
....
....
....
....
....
....

The person in your family
who has impacted me the most is:

The person in my family
who has impacted you the most is:

LOOKS LIKE
>>> WE <<<
MADE IT!

♥ ANNIVERSARY ♥

Our anniversary date:

....

How we celebrated our first anniversary:

....

....

....

....

....

....

....

....

....

....

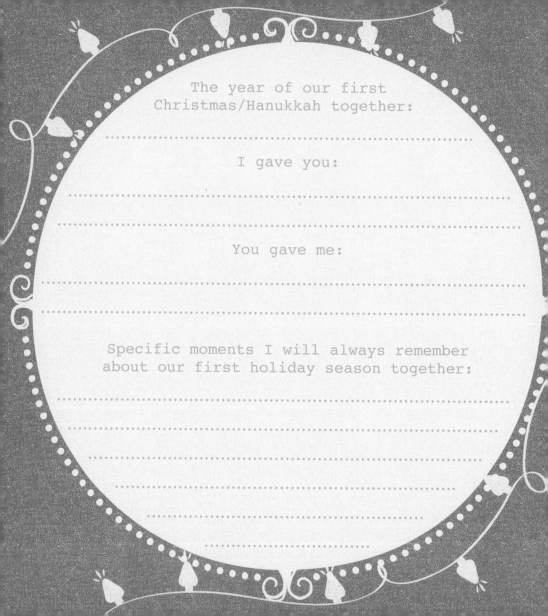

The year of our first
Christmas/Hanukkah together:

....

I gave you:

....

....

You gave me:

....

....

Specific moments I will always remember
about our first holiday season together:

....

....

....

....

....

The most memorable gifts
you've ever given me:

....

....

....

....

....

The most memorable things
or events you've
surprised me with:

....

....

....

....

....

....

GOOD TIMES, BAD TIMES,
YOU KNOW
I HAD MY
SHARE

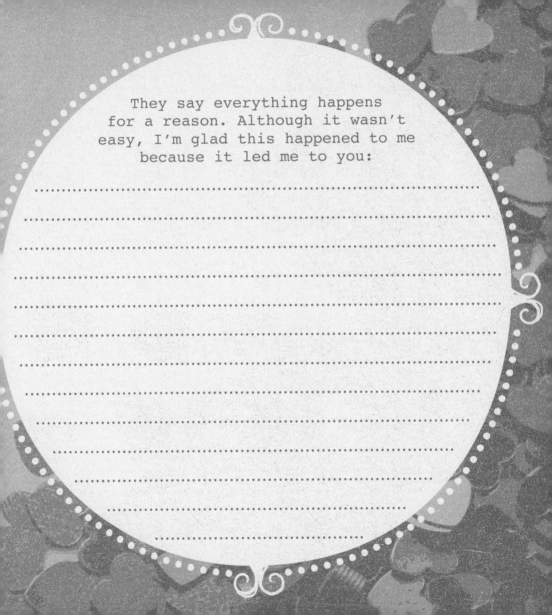

They say everything happens
for a reason. Although it wasn't
easy, I'm glad this happened to me
because it led me to you:

....

....

....

....

....

....

....

....

....

....

Like every couple, we
have weathered a few storms
together. Here are some important
lessons I've learned:

....

....

....

....

....

....

....

....

....

....

....

....

WELL,
I WON'T GIVE UP ON US,
EVEN IF THE SKIES GET ROUGH

Every successful relationship involves
sacrifices. These are the things
I have sacrificed for you:

....

....

....

....

....

....

....

....

....

....

....

....

....

These are the things
you have sacrificed for me:

....
....
....
....
....
....
....
....
....
....
....
....
....
....
....

Over time, our relationship has changed
in many ways. These are the aspects of our
relationship that I hope will never change:

....

....

....

....

....

....

....

....

....

....

....

....

....

These are the aspects of our
relationship that I hope we can work on:

....

....

....

....

....

....

....

....

....

....

....

....

SOME DAYS
WE FORGET
TO LOOK AROUND US.
SOME DAYS
WE CAN'T SEE
THE JOY
THAT SURROUNDS US.

HOW WONDERFUL LIFE IS

while YOU're in the

WORLD

Cherish *the* Present

Chapter 2

These are the things you do
that take my breath away:

....
....
....
....
....
....
....
....
....
....
....
....
....
....
....
....

I still get butterflies in my stomach when you:

....

....

....

....

....

....

....

{A drawing of how I feel when you do that.}

Three things I admire most about you are:

1.
....

....

2.
....

....

3.
....

....

These are just some of the many ways
you help make me a better person:

....

....

....

....

....

....

....

The things I find most attractive about you are:

The things you find most attractive about me are:

I belong with you. You belong with me. You're my sweetheart.

These are the reasons I
truly believe we belong together:

....

....

....

....

....

....

....

....

....

....

....

....

Here is something
I've never told you about myself:

....

....

....

....

....

....

....

....

....

....

....

FIVE THINGS THAT WE SHOULD FOREVER KEEP BETWEEN THE TWO OF US:

Our life philosophies are
compatible in these ways:

....

....

....

....

....

....

....

....

My favorite life motto:

....

....

Your favorite life motto:

....

....

....

The ways our political views overlap:

The ways our political views differ:

....
....
....
....
....
....
....
....
....

The ways our views
on religion and
spirituality
overlap:

....

....

....

....

....

....

....

....

....

....

....

....

The ways our views
on religion and
spirituality
differ:

....

....

....

....

....

....

....

....

....

....

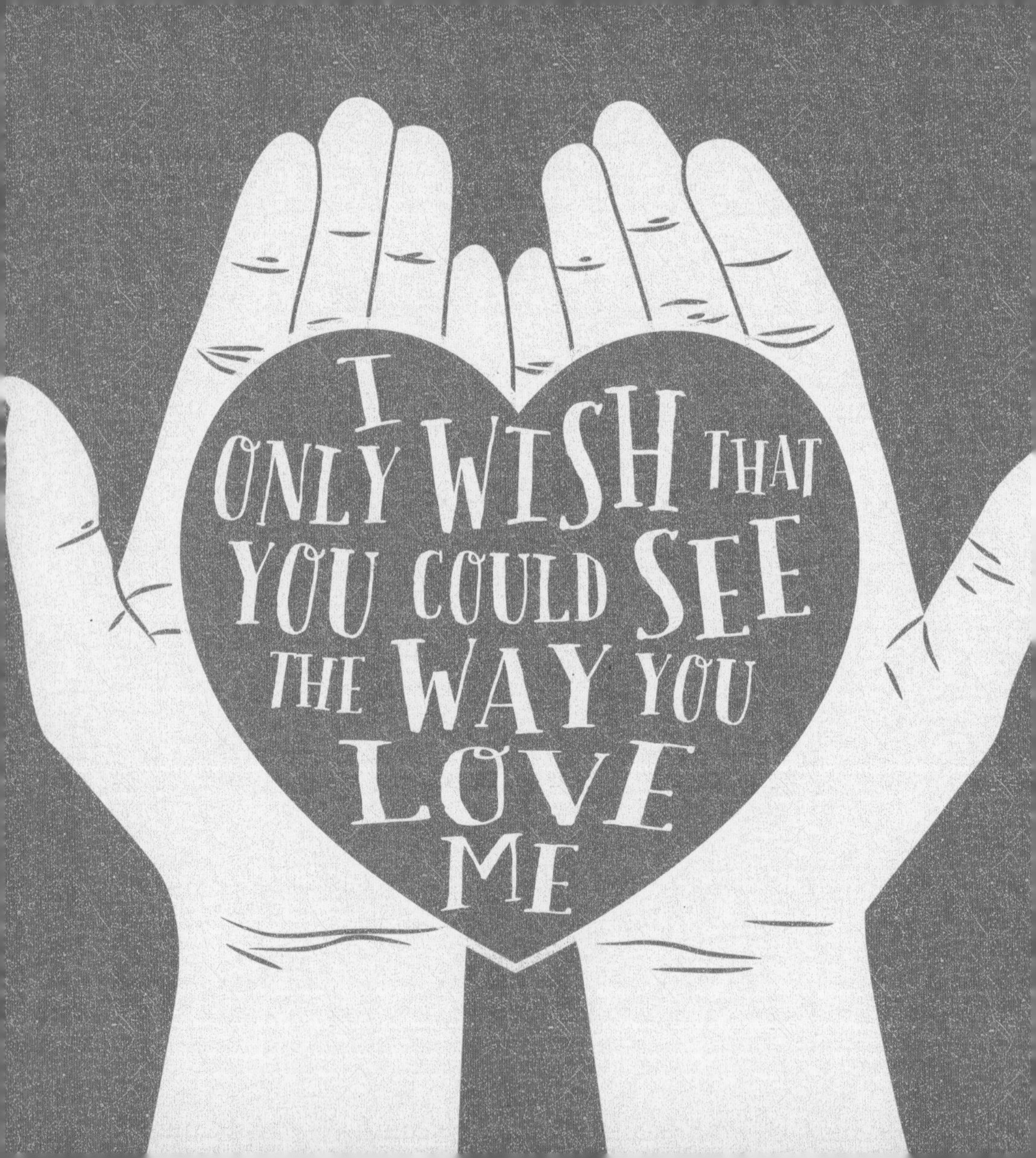
I ONLY WISH THAT YOU COULD SEE THE WAY YOU LOVE ME

There are five basic ways to show *affection.*

This is how I would rank them, with "1" being the most important:

☐ Touch

☐ Quality Time

☐ Gifts

☐ Acts of Kindness

☐ Words of Affection

My favorite way to show you that I love you is:

I love these little favors
that you do for me:

....

....

....

....

....

....

....

....

....

....

....

....

I try to make your life
easier by:

....

....

....

....

....

....

....

....

....

....

....

....

....

I COULDN'T LOVE YOU ANY BETTER. I LOVE YOU JUST THE WAY YOU ARE.

Here are five adjectives I would use
to describe you:

___ Adventurous	___ Easygoing	___ Patient
___ Affectionate	___ Funny	___ Philosophical
___ Agreeable	___ Generous	___ Reserved
___ Ambitious	___ Honest	___ Respectful
___ Charming	___ Humble	___ Romantic
___ Chivalrous	___ Intelligent	___ Sophisticated
___ Compassionate	___ Intuitive	___ Spontaneous
___ Courageous	___ Loyal	___ Stylish
___ Creative	___ Optimistic	___ Thoughtful
___ Dutiful	___ Outgoing	___ Warmhearted

These are the five adjectives I think
you would use to describe me:

1. ....

2. ....

3. ....

4. ....

5. ....

MY HEART IS DRENCHED IN WINE BUT YOU'LL BE ON MY MIND FOREVER

Our relationship is most like:

___ A fine wine (it keeps getting better with age)
___ Coffee (sprightly and playful)
___ Lemonade (a tangy mix of sweet and sour)
___ Beer (cold and frothy with bite)
___ Tea (warm and nurturing)
___ Chai latte (smooth and exotic)

Three words I would use to describe
our relationship are:

1.

2.

3.

If our love story were a movie,
this celebrity would play me:

....

....

This celebrity would play you:

....

....

The title and subtitle would be:

....

....

The surprise twist at the end would be:

....

....

....

....

....

When our movie wins an Academy Award,
we will thank these people during
our acceptance speeches:

....

....

....

....

....

....

....

....

....

....

....

....

....

IN OTHER WORDS,
HOLD MY HAND.
IN OTHER WORDS,
BABY, KISS ME.

Terms of endearment we use for each other:

___ Angel	___ Bunny	___ Love
___ Babe	___ Doll	___ Sweetheart
___ Baby	___ Dear	___ Sweetie
___ Beautiful	___ Handsome	___ Sugar
___ Boo	___ Honey	___ Other: _____

My special nickname for you:

Your special nickname for me:

My favorite holiday to spend with you is:

___ Valentine's Day   ___ Thanksgiving
___ St. Patrick's Day   ___ Christmas
___ Easter   ___ Hanukkah
___ Fourth of July   ___ New Year's Eve
___ Halloween   ___ Other: _____

A holiday memory I will always hold
dear to my heart is:

....

....

....

....

....

....

....

....

....

It's
always better

❧ when we're together ❧

In the summer, I love it when we:

....
....
....
....
....
....

My favorite part of fall with you is:

....
....
....
....
....
....

Winter is the perfect time for us to:

....

....

....

....

....

....

In the spring, I have a blast when we:

....

....

....

....

....

....

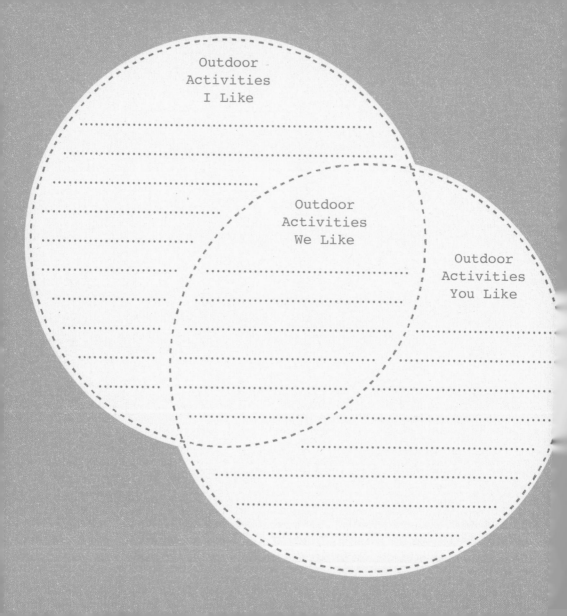

Outdoor
Activities
I Like

Outdoor
Activities
We Like

Outdoor
Activities
You Like

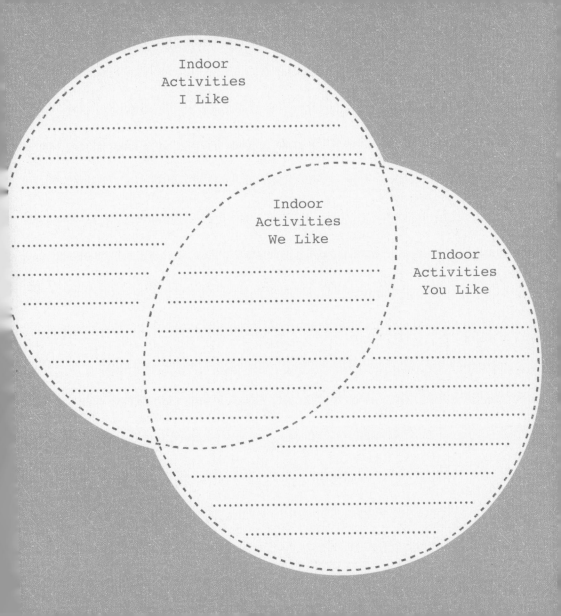

Indoor
Activities
I Like

Indoor
Activities
We Like

Indoor
Activities
You Like

When we have an
entire day all to ourselves,
this is how we like to spend it:

....

....

....

....

....

....

....

....

....

....

....

....

....

YOUR LOVE IS BETTER THAN

ICE CREAM

Better than anything else that I've tried

≫⟩OUR⟨≪
FAVORITE RESTAURANT IS

I usually order:

....
....

You usually order:

....
....

A favorite memory at this restaurant:

....
....
....
....
....

Foods I Like

Foods We Like

Foods You Like

WE HAVE ENRICHED EACH OTHER'S LIVES BY SHARING THE WONDERFUL PEOPLE WE KNOW.

I'm thankful to have met these friends through you:

....
....
....
....
....
....
....
....

A favorite memory of time we've spent with these friends:

....
....
....
....
....
....
....

Friends you've met through me:

··
··
··
··
··
··
··

A favorite memory of time
we've spent with these friends

··
··
··
··
··
··
··
··
··

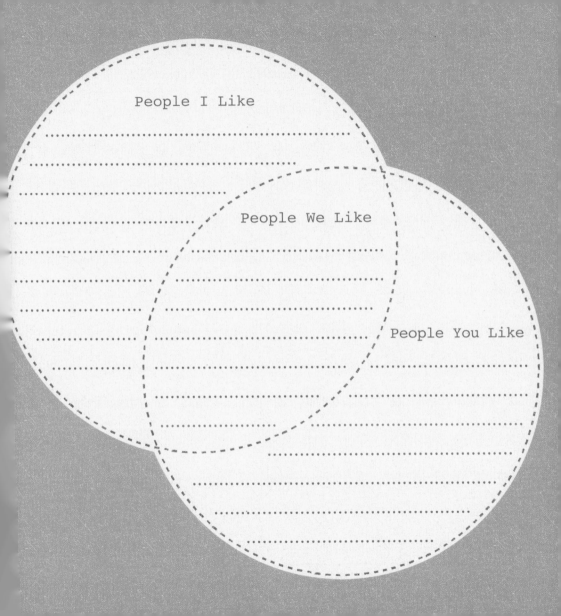

People I Like

People We Like

People You Like

Each moment with you is just like a DREAM to me that somehow came TRUE

Treasure *the* Big Moments

Chapter 3

♥ ENGAGEMENT ♥

We became engaged on:

....

Details I will always remember about
that special moment:

....

....

....

....

....

....

....

....

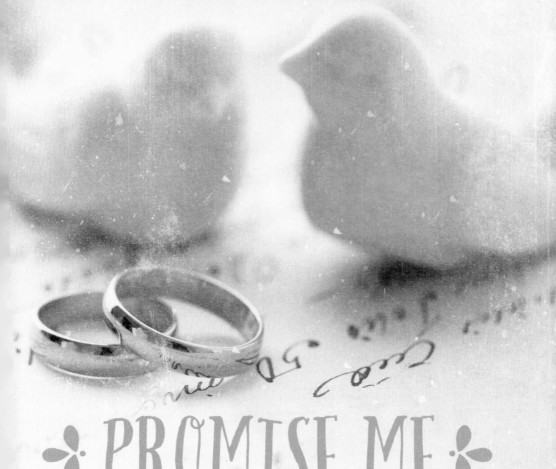

PROMISE ME

YOU'LL ALWAYS BE HAPPY BY MY SIDE

♥ WEDDING DAY ♥

Our wedding date:..

The wedding took place at: ....

The reception took place at: ....

Maid of Honor:..

Bridesmaids: ....

....

Flower Girl: ....

Best Man: ....

Groomsmen: ....

....

Ring Bearer: ....

Other members of the wedding party:....................................

....

....

Details I will always remember
about our wedding day:

....

....

....

....

....

....

....

....

....

....

....

....

....

....

OUR HONEYMOON DESTINATION:

Details I will always remember about our honeymoon:

....

....

....

....

....

....

....

....

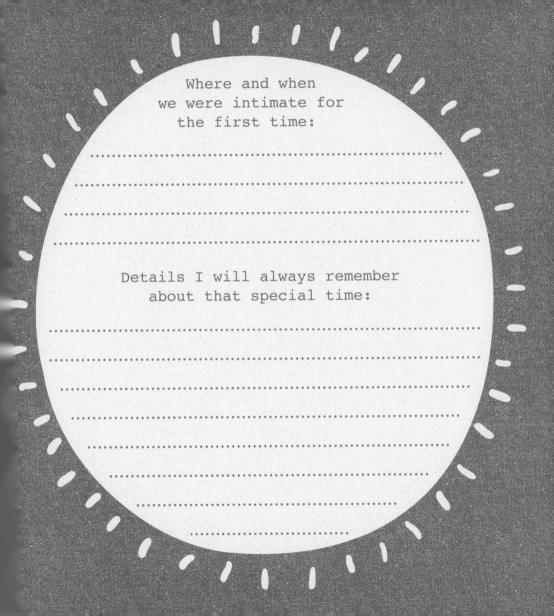

Where and when
we were intimate for
the first time:

....

....

....

....

Details I will always remember
about that special time:

....

....

....

....

....

....

....

....

Our first home together:

....

....

....

Details I will always remember
about moving in together:

....

....

....

....

....

....

....

....

....

The best things about living together:

....
....
....
....
....
....

The most difficult things about
living together:

....
....
....
....
....

THE BEST

is yet to come,

and won't that be

FINE?

Toast to the Future

Chapter 4

My dream career is:

....
....
....
....
....
....
....

Your dream career is:

....
....
....
....
....
....
....
....
....

We will always
make special time
for "us" by:

....
....
....
....
....
....
....

Our dream vacation is in:

Things we want to do and see:

....

....

....

....

....

....

....

....

....

....

HOME SWEET HOME

Our dream home is in or near the:

__ Beach   __ Desert   __ Suburbs

__ City   __ Forest   __ Tropics

__ Countryside   __ Mountains   __ Other:_____

The style of our home would be:

__ Art Deco   __ Craftsman Bungalow   __ Ranch House

__ Beach House   __ Farm House   __ Spanish

__ Brownstone   __ Igloo   __ Tudor Revival

__ Cape Cod   __ Log Cabin   __ Tuscan

__ Castle   __ Mansion   __ Victorian

__ Colonial Revival   __ Mediterranean   __ Zen

__ Contemporary   __ Mid-20th Century   __ Other:_____

Must-have features in our dream home:

....

....

....

....

....

....

FAMILY

We are looking forward to:

___ A large family   ___ A life of just the two of us
___ A small family   ___ Whatever happens

Types of pets:

....

....

Ideal number of children: Boys_____ Girls_____

What we will name our pets and/or children:

Names I Like   Names You Like

Names
We Like

PRICELESS

I DON'T CARE
TOO MUCH FOR MONEY.
MONEY CAN'T BUY ME LOVE.

IF WE WIN THE LOTTERY SOMEDAY,

I'll buy you: ....

....

....

You'll buy me: ....

....

We'll put the following plan into place to protect our relationship: ....

....

....

....

When we retire, I'd like to live in:

....

You'd like to live in:

....

We'll probably end up living in:

....

The best part about retirement will be:

....

....

....

....

....

....

....

....

....

....

WE'LL FAST FORWARD
TO A FEW YEARS LATER,
AND NO ONE KNOWS
EXCEPT THE BOTH OF US

{OUR "BUCKET LIST"}

Places we want to visit:

- [ ] _____
- [ ] _____
- [ ] _____
- [ ] _____
- [ ] _____
- [ ] _____

- [ ] _____
- [ ] _____
- [ ] _____
- [ ] _____
- [ ] _____
- [ ] _____

Skills we want to acquire:

- [ ] _____
- [ ] _____
- [ ] _____
- [ ] _____
- [ ] _____
- [ ] _____

- [ ] _____
- [ ] _____
- [ ] _____
- [ ] _____
- [ ] _____

Activities we want to try:

☐ _____
☐ _____   ☐ _____
☐ _____   ☐ _____
☐ _____   ☐ _____
☐ _____   ☐ _____
☐ _____   ☐ _____
☐ _____

Goals we want to accomplish:

☐ _____
☐ _____   ☐ _____
☐ _____   ☐ _____
☐ _____   ☐ _____
☐ _____   ☐ _____
☐ _____   ☐ _____
☐ _____

LOVE LETTERS
STRAIGHT FROM
YOUR HEART,
KEEP US SO NEAR
WHILE APART

{A Love Letter from Me to You}

{A Photo of Us}

Truly Madly Deeply

Irvine, CA 92618
PH: 949-727-0800 • StudioOh.com
Produced by the creative team at Studio Oh!
Walter Robertson, Art Director
Stacy H. Kim, Designer/Illustrator
S.J. Allison, Editor

Prompts written by Elizabeth T. Gilbert

Song Lyrics Credits:
Page 2, written by Tim Rice-Oxley, "Somewhere Only We Know," © 2004. Page 5, written by Mack Gordon and Harry Warren, "At Last," © 1941. Page 8, written by Alan Jay Lerner, "I Could Have Danced All Night," © 1956. Page 10, written by Guy Garvey, "Mirrorball," © 2008. Page 13, written by George David Weiss, Hugo Peretti, and Luigi Creatore, "Can't Help Falling in Love," © 1961. Page 18, written by Robert Ellis and Taylor Swift, "I'm Only Me (When I'm with You)," © 2007. Page 24, written by Robert Seger, James Morrison, John Densmore, and Raymond Manzarek, "People Are Strange," © 1967. Page 28, written by Shania Twain and Robert John Lange, "Still the One," © 1997. Page 32, written by John Bonham, John Paul Jones, and Jimmy Page, "Good Times, Bad Times," © 1969. Page 35, written by Jason Mraz and Michael Natter, "I Won't Give Up," © 2012. Page 40, written by Carole Bayer Sager, David W. Foster, and Richard J. Page, "Thankful," © 2007. Page 42, written by Bernie Taupin, "Your Song," © 1970. Page 44, written by David Grohl, "Everlong," © 1997. Page 49, written by Linda Perry, "Beautiful," © 2002. Page 52, written by Wesley Keith Schultz and Jeremiah Fraites, "Ho Hey," © 2012. Page 56, written by Stevie Wonder, "You Are the Sunshine of My Life," © 1972. Page 62, written by Keith Follese, "The Way You Love Me," © 1999. Page 66, written by William Martin Joel, "Just the Way You Are," © 1977. Page 68, written by Jesse Harris, "Don't Know Why," © 2002. Page 72, written by Bart Howard, "Fly Me to the Moon (In Other Words)," © 1954. Page 75, written by Jack Hody Johnson, "Better Together," © 2005. Page 81, written by Sarah McLachlan, "Ice Cream," © 1993. Page 84, written by Kurt Cobain, "Lithium," © 1991. Page 88, written by Rod Temperton, "Always and Forever," © 1976. Page 91, written by Pat Monahan, "Marry Me," © 2009. Page 98, written by Carolyn Leigh, "The Best Is Yet to Come," © 1959. Page 104, written by John Lennon and Paul McCartney, "Can't Buy Me Love," © 1964. Page 107, written by Alanis Morissette, "Hands Clean," © 2002. Page 110, written by Edward Heyman, "Love Letters," © 1957.

Item #86402 • ISBN 978-1-62226-593-0
Recyclable. Printed with soy-based ink.
Printed in Korea

3 5 7 9 8 6 4